TEEN MOGUL

A full-length dramedy by
Lucy Wang

www.youthplays.com
info@youthplays.com
424-703-5315

CAST OF CHARACTERS

TRACY, 15, any ethnicity.

ALEX, 13, Tracy's brother. Can also play Shareholder, Male Teen on Video.

HENRY, Tracy's father, also Shareholder.

SARAH NUTTER, Tracy's English teacher at Kucinich High. Can also play Shareholder, Shop Owner, part of Couple in Video, Rita Storey.

MALE TEEN ON VIDEO, free spirit guitar player.

OLIVER WILCOX, president of Buckeye Bank and Kevin's father. Can also play Shareholder, part of Couple in Video, Duke.

KEVIN WILCOX, Tracy's classmate, also Shareholder.

CHRISTOPHER BRENNAN, CEO of Advance, Incorporated.

MARINA, product designer, any ethnicity. Can also play Shareholder.

RITA STOREY, news reporter, can be played by Sarah Nutter.

DUKE MANNING, venture capitalist, corporate raider, can be played by Oliver or Henry.

SIX SHAREHOLDERS, played by above, or separately.

COUPLE IN VIDEO, can be played by Sarah Nutter & Oliver, or separately.

COMPANY OWNER, can be played by Oliver or Sarah Nutter.

Teen Mogul allows for a maximum cast of 20, but can be played with a minimum of 8 as reflected above.

PRODUCTION NOTES

Settings are meant to be suggested and the action fluid. Set in Ohio. For performance of copyrighted songs, arrangements or recordings mentioned in this play, the permission of the copyright owner(s) must be obtained. Other songs, arrangements or recordings may be substituted provided permission from the copyright owner(s) of such songs, arrangements or recordings is obtained; or songs, arrangements or recordings in the public domain may be substituted.

ACT I

SCENE 1

(Tracy's house, full lights. TRACY, ALEX and HENRY try to stay busy and positive. Dialogue is "fast." The light gradually changes from full brightness, to three-quarters, to half to complete blackout at the end of scene.)

TRACY: Maybe we should call the police.

HENRY: No police. We are not troublemakers.

TRACY: But she's never late. She never misses dinner.

ALEX: Officer, my mother didn't cook me dinner tonight, so something bad must have happened. Fast food, son. Officer, my family doesn't eat junk food. No junk food, son, are you sure you're American? Shut up and eat this donut, son. It will change your life, and how you feel about your mother.

TRACY: Newsflash. Cops are not known for their sense of humor.

ALEX: How much you wanna bet I can make a cop laugh?

TRACY: And see you go to jail?

HENRY: She probably got detained. Railroaded by some parent whose kid is failing, and can't get into Harvard. Boo hoo hoo. We can't all go to Harvard. Cry me a river.

ALEX: I'm gonna quote you on that, Dad.

HENRY: They can't all go to Harvard because you're going to Harvard, and there's just not enough room at the top.

ALEX: Or, on the road. Do you think she was in a car accident?

TRACY: I'm calling the police.

HENRY: And draw more unwanted attention to ourselves?

TRACY: More? I wasn't aware we had any.

HENRY: Don't act dumb. How do you think this is going to look?

ALEX: That mom is a bad driver?

HENRY: I've acquired some speeding tickets.

ALEX: Speed racer. Zoom zoom.

HENRY: Life in the fast lane. It adds up.

TRACY: How much?

ALEX: We're over-reacting. From hunger.

HENRY: Alex is right. Our stomachs have turned us into chicken livers. Make us dinner.

TRACY: Dinner? Now?

ALEX: Tracy, I'm really, really hungry.

HENRY: Starving.

TRACY: How can you two be hungry at a time like this?

HENRY: Who knows? That's probably why we can't think straight, we need food. Delicious mouth-watering food.

ALEX: Times like this I could really use some comfort food.

TRACY: So, call Luigi's and order a pizza. What is this, 1492? You have fingers. A cell phone.

HENRY: Pizza? Do you know how many calories are in a pizza?

ALEX: Thousands! Per slice. You trying to kill us?

HENRY: Is that any way to show your family some compassion?

TRACY: You're sending me into the kitchen because I'm a girl?

ALEX: No, silly. It's because we live in Ohio. A swing state. One foot in, one foot out. Swing with me.

HENRY: Think of my command as a gift. Master chefs are welcome everywhere.

TRACY: Unbelievable. In this day and age, what I'm hearing. You two should be ashamed.

ALEX: For wanting to help you help others? Admit it, Tracy, you're hungry too.

HENRY: There's no shame in hunger. In fact, we should celebrate.

TRACY: What the? Celebrate what?

ALEX: Celebrate O-HI-OH. Let's all join hands and swing, shall we? C'mon, Buckeyes, buck up. With God, All Things Are Possible. It's the Ohio State motto.

(Alex, Tracy, Henry join hands, and swing as the light changes several times, then dim. Tracy steps out, spotlight on Tracy.)

TRACY: There we were, swinging back and forth, doing the hokey pokey, mixing it up, turning it all around. Hand, foot, heart. Putting it in, taking it out. My mother loves me, loves me not, loves me, loves me not. She loves me, yeah yeah yeah. She hates me yeah, yeah yeah until finally, all the lights went completely out. Blackout. The end. Of. Us. As We Knew It.

(End of Scene 1.)

SCENE 2

(One month later. Like a Magritte painting. Darkness [rain/ominous clouds] inside, Daylight [sun] outside. DOOR KNOCKING. Alex, Tracy and Henry in separate dark spaces.)

HENRY: Go away! Read the frigging sign. No solicitors.

ALEX: Take the junk mail, leave the thin mints.

TRACY: Wait. Did somebody order pizza? I think I smell pepperoni.

ALEX: Pepperoni. There is a God.

HENRY: What's this obsession with pizza? Pizza is party food. We're in no mood for a party.

ALEX: Seriously, what good is food when you're dead inside?

(KNOCKING continues. Louder.)

HENRY: Did someone leave the light on because someone is not getting the message! Numbskull! Idiot! Go away!

TRACY: Don't scream, Dad. Dead giveaway we're home.

HENRY: Oh yeah. Sssh. Sit still.

ALEX: Total darkness here. Tracy? Are you reading? Tracy.

TRACY: *(Turns off her e-book reader light:)* You need to do something when your heart is broken.

HENRY: I know, kids! Turn on that awful music I hate. Turn it on real loud.

ALEX: What kind of music?

HENRY: You know, the kind I hate. Loud. Obnoxious. Heavy.

ALEX: Eminem? Radiohead? Arctic Monkeys?

HENRY: Songs with scary lyrics that pierce daggers straight through your soul.

TRACY: Taylor Swift.

ALEX: Oh yes, these boots were made for walking.

HENRY: Just pick one offensive song. Please.

TRACY: Just so much music in the world, Dad.

HENRY: And no love. None of her favorites. Nothing that reminds me of her. Nothing is mine.

ALEX: Mother loved all music. Now what? Tracy?

TRACY: What about one of your favorite angry comedians? Full of vim and venom.

ALEX: One that drops the F bomb a lot? F this, F that. I don't Effing Think So. F me, well, F U!

TRACY: Sure to offend whoever's at the door.

PERSON AT THE DOOR: *(Off:)* Not me. Open up. Or I'm calling child services.

HENRY: Child services?

ALEX: They're bluffing. Nobody wants us.

TRACY: I think I recognize that voice.

HENRY: Crank it up, son. Full blast. Batter those eardrums.

(Alex chooses some MUSIC and cranks it up. The PERSON AT THE DOOR cranks it up too with Eminem's "I'm Not Afraid.")

ALEX: Are you kidding me? You're not supposed to swing with the enemy.

TRACY: *(Singing along:)* I'm Not Afraid, I'm Not Afraid To Take a Stand, To Take a Stand.

HENRY: Turn it off, Alex.

ALEX: What if it's the police? Maybe a neighbor complained. In dry air, sound moves at 768 miles per hour.

HENRY: Tracy, get the door.

TRACY: Why me? Is this because I'm a girl, or because we live in a swing state?

ALEX: Because you're a girl, stupid.

HENRY: I'm in my bathrobe. Unkempt.

TRACY: I'm not exactly looking my best either.

ALEX: Bet you smell better. I haven't showered in a week.

TRACY: Gross. How can you stand yourself?

ALEX: Can anyone in this house honestly stand themselves?

HENRY: Tracy, please. Get the door.

TRACY: But what if this person is...armed and dangerous?

HENRY: You're a girl. Who wants to hurt a girl?

TRACY: Get in back of the line.

ALEX: Downward facing lemur. They'll take pity.

(Tracy opens door slowly. She immediately recognizes the face, slams door, straightens her hair, takes deep breath.)

TRACY: Miss Nutter.

MISS NUTTER: I brought you pizza.

ALEX: *(Takes the pizza:)* Oh my god. There is a Santa Claus. Thank you.

TRACY: This is so not a good time.

MISS NUTTER: It's never a good time when your mother leaves.

TRACY: Excuse me? Who told you that?

MISS NUTTER: You heard me, Tracy, we need to talk.

TRACY: There's nothing to talk about.

MISS NUTTER: Of course there is. We have your whole future to discuss.

TRACY: What future?

MISS NUTTER: That's why you have to let me in. I'm not leaving until you see what I see.

TRACY: Perhaps another time.

MISS NUTTER: I gave you fair warning. *(Miss Nutter whips out her cell phone:)* Connect me to child services, please.

HENRY: Please let the pesky intruder in!

(Tracy lets Miss Nutter in.)

TRACY: The place is a mess.

MISS NUTTER: As to be expected at a time like this.

TRACY: How did you find out?

MISS NUTTER: Tracy, please, the whole school knows.

TRACY: The whole school?

MISS NUTTER: Maybe the whole town.

TRACY: Oh, no. I feel sick.

ALEX: Sound travels about 768 miles per hour. How big is this town?

MISS NUTTER: Not very.

HENRY: See why we cannot show our face? Everybody knows she left us.

MISS NUTTER: For two seconds, then it's forgotten. Yesterday's news. It's an A.D.D. world. Next!

HENRY: You're depressing.

TRACY: Dad, this is my English teacher. Miss Nutter.

HENRY: Naturally. Always the English teachers that cause the most trouble.

MISS NUTTER: I'll take that as a compliment. Sarah.

HENRY: *(Shakes Miss Nutter's hand:)* Henry.

ALEX: *(Thrusting his hand:)* Alex.

MISS NUTTER: *(Shakes Alex's hand gently:)* I've heard so much about you.

ALEX: Only the good things are true.

MISS NUTTER: Naturally.

ALEX: Would you like some hot green tea? It's rich in anti-oxidants.

MISS NUTTER: Sure.

ALEX: Tracy, you heard our guest. Brew.

MISS NUTTER: Alex.

ALEX: Just kidding. I'll brew you some.
> *(Alex exits.)*

TRACY: Forgive him; he thinks he's funny.

MISS NUTTER: He's definitely funny.

ALEX: *(Off:)* Told you.

HENRY: He's going to Harvard.

MISS NUTTER: Great. What about Tracy?

HENRY: What all girls do. Go to college, get married, have babies–

TRACY: Until then, cook, clean, study. Not necessarily in that order.

MISS NUTTER: Henry, have you thought of family therapy?

HENRY: Therapy? Therapy is for crazy people. Are you calling us crazy?

TRACY: Miss Nutter, please.

HENRY: You can't come over to our house and call us crazy.

MISS NUTTER: You've all been through such a traumatic experience. Sometimes...

HENRY: No time.

MISS NUTTER: ...it takes a professional.

HENRY: We don't need your help.

MISS NUTTER: Nothing wrong with–

HENRY: Asking you to leave.

MISS NUTTER: How about medication?

HENRY: Medication!

MISS NUTTER: Xanax. Lunesta. Wellbutrin. Ambien. Plenty of options.

HENRY: Tracy. Your English teacher is recommending a wild assortment of drugs.

MISS NUTTER: Just a temporary helper. There's no shame in asking for a little help.

HENRY: Peddling drugs. Shame on you.

(Alex returns with teapot and teacups.)

ALEX: If you haven't noticed, our family likes our pain full force. No cream, no sugar.

MISS NUTTER: No reason to prolong the agony. The disarray. If you can feel better sooner, why wouldn't you want to?

TRACY: Miss Nutter, it's only natural we're in tremendous pain. What would you do without your mother? We may be hurting, but we're not crazy.

MISS NUTTER: I agree. But tell me, how are you going to get through this? This mess. It's worse than a pigsty around here. Sorry.

HENRY: None of this is any of your business.

MISS NUTTER: But it is.

HENRY: How so?

ALEX: Yes, how so?

MISS NUTTER: Health department.

HENRY: We'll clean up. Soon as you leave. Won't we, Tracy?

TRACY: *(Starts cleaning up:)* Immediately. We'll all pitch in, right, Alex? Great American Clean Up.

ALEX: Isn't that women's work?

MISS NUTTER: And that stack of mail. I bet a lot of those are unpaid bills. Nobody writes letters any more.

HENRY: I'll get to it.

MISS NUTTER: When? Next year?

HENRY: It is a federal offense to tamper with the U.S. mails, Sarah.

MISS NUTTER: It's also a crime to allow your family to completely fall apart, Henry. "Thou shall not kill" includes your family. As the head of the household, you need to lead. Inspire. Set an example.

HENRY: We're not falling apart.

MISS NUTTER: Oh, really? Alex barely shows up at school. And when he does, it's to act up.

HENRY: Is this true, Alex? You cutting school?

ALEX: Why should I go to school? What's the point? It's not like you're going to work. Monkey see, monkey do.

MISS NUTTER: Is this what you want for your Harvard-bound son?

HENRY: *(Covering for Alex:)* He's needed here.

ALEX: You barely know me. What do you care?

MISS NUTTER: I'm an English teacher, I care.

HENRY: Oh, the humanities. Woe is me.

MISS NUTTER: Yes, woe is you, for I know your daughter quite well. Well enough to recognize Tracy is capable of doing anything she sets her sights on. Anything.

TRACY: Anything?

MISS NUTTER: Anything you set your heart on.

ALEX: What about me, and my heart?

MISS NUTTER: You said I barely know you, but if I had to guess, I'd have to guess that you are just as capable as your sister.

ALEX: Capable of what?

MISS NUTTER: Find out at school.

ALEX: Great. A trap.

MISS NUTTER: So if you don't clean up your act, Henry, I am going to report you for child abuse.

HENRY: Oh please. I'd like to see you try.

MISS NUTTER: Fine. I'll drag you through the mud if I have to. You are not going to ruin your children's lives. Not if I can help it. I want Tracy and Alex back in school, full throttle. First thing Monday morning, Tracy, my office, bring your revised business plan.

ALEX: Business plan. Are we talking about the same Tracy?

HENRY: You have a business plan?

TRACY: I used to. You know, before Mother left. It's irrelevant now.

MISS NUTTER: Not true, Miss Tracy. You need a business plan more than ever.

TRACY: Why?

MISS NUTTER: What do you mean, why? Isn't it obvious? I cannot bear to see you waste your gifts, Tracy. I cannot bear to watch you throw it all away over a mother who didn't deserve you. There, I said it.

HENRY: What gifts, what dreams? Tracy. What is she talking about?

MISS NUTTER: Do you have any idea who your daughter is?

HENRY: Are you her drug dealer?

MISS NUTTER: She's an Icarus in a world of Babbitts.

HENRY: She's fifteen.

TRACY: Miss Nutter, he doesn't believe. And probably never will.

MISS NUTTER: Tell him anyways.

ALEX: Humor me.

TRACY: I want to make the cover of a national magazine, run my own company, and write a great American novel.

ALEX: Gee, is that all? Why don't you just run for President?

TRACY: And win a big literary prize.

ALEX: Pie. In. The. Sky.

HENRY: Girls. Always multi-tasking.

TRACY: I know. I'm not very clear-headed. Being motherless and all, I'm doomed. I'll never make it.

MISS NUTTER: Nonsense. Total B.S. Remember our unit on Langston Hughes. Tracy, what happens to a dream deferred?

TRACY: Does it dry up like a raisin in the sun?

MISS NUTTER: Or fester like a sore. And then run.

TRACY: Does it stink like rotting meat?

MISS NUTTER: Or crust and sugar over—like a syrupy sweet?

TRACY: Maybe it just sags like a heavy load.

MISS NUTTER: Or does it explode?

(BIG EXPLOSION.)

(End of Scene 2.)

SCENE 3

(Middle of the night, after Miss Nutter's visit. Tracy panics as she sifts through the pile of large [in size as well as amount for dramatic effect, like those big cardboard checks] unpaid bills.)

TRACY: Mother, how could you do this to us? What did we do? What did I do?

(Alex enters.)

ALEX: She buried us deep, didn't she?

TRACY: Probably a clerical mistake. Administrative error.

ALEX: Liar.

(Alex fights Tracy for the bill and eventually wins.)

We're three months overdue on our mortgage, and if the bank doesn't receive immediate payment, the bank will be forced to initiate foreclosure proceedings. Are you kidding me?

TRACY: We'll get it straightened out tomorrow. Soon as the bank opens.

ALEX: Motherless and homeless, I've become one sad afterschool special.

TRACY: Dad will know what to do. He always knows what to do.

ALEX: Yeah, right. Like he knew how to stop her from leaving.

TRACY: Have ye a little faith.

ALEX: I have more faith in you.

TRACY: You do? Why?

ALEX: No teacher has ever paid me a special visit and told me I was gifted.

TRACY: There's still time. I am a little older.

ALEX: You're supposed to be my role model?

TRACY: I'm trying.

ALEX: That's why my money's on you. If I had any money.

TRACY: If I only knew how.

ALEX: Fine. Why don't we just ask him?

TRACY: At this hour?

ALEX: He's not sleeping. Bet you any money he's wide-awake.

TRACY: We could just check the bank balances ourselves.

ALEX: We can? You know where Dad hides the checkbook and his passwords for online accounts?

TRACY: Mom told me. One day, after one of their legendary fights. He stores the password info in John Dos Passos' book, *The Big Money*.

(Points to book.)

ALEX: I see you have the book right there. Let's do it.

TRACY: Maybe we should just ask Dad.

ALEX: You're afraid.

TRACY: Alex, what are we going to do?

ALEX: We?

TRACY: There must be something we can do. A job we can get?

ALEX: Who's going to hire me? I'm 13, a very unlucky number. A number most people tend to avoid, skip over. Pretend doesn't exist.

TRACY: LeAnn Rimes was only 13 when her album *Blue* climbed to #1 on the Top Country Charts and went platinum. Steve Jobs was given up for adoption, dropped out of college, and changed the world. Jim Carrey was 12 when his father lost his job, and they went from middle class to complete poverty. Just like us. We could live in a van, if we had to, and still hit it big. We just have to have faith.

ALEX: We have to have faith because we have no money, do we? You already checked the balances, didn't you? You know.

TRACY: I had to.

ALEX: Mother took off with a lot of money, didn't she? We're screwed.

TRACY: See, you're gifted. You just need to apply yourself more, and bring it home.

ALEX: Nice try. How much?

TRACY: Maybe we can help Dad ask for a humongous raise?

ALEX: In this economy? After he's missed so much work?

TRACY: His boss is divorced, too.

ALEX: So we're going to milk the boss for some sympathy, are we?

TRACY: Sympathy for the Devil.

ALEX: Speaking of–

(Henry struts out in his PJs, empty bottle of Scotch in his hand.)

HENRY: I wish I'd never set foot in this country, never married that witch, never agreed to have children. Please, God, let me go, I have nothing to live for. Please take me out of my misery, I just want to die.

(He falls to his knees.)

ALEX: There goes the idea Father Knows Best.

(Tracy and Alex, devastated, also drop to the floor.)

(End of Scene 3.)

SCENE 4

(Buckeye Bank, next day. Portraits of old rich white men hang from the ceiling, dangling and judging. President of the Bank, OLIVER, is in the corner, looking very rich, super confident. Henry wants to bolt, but Tracy forces him to stay.)

HENRY: Please, I just want to die.

TRACY: We didn't come to America to live on the street. In cardboard boxes. Is that what you want your obituary to say? He died in a refrigerator box.

HENRY: I died of a broken heart. No shame in that.

TRACY: No shame in renegotiating a mortgage either. A lot of people survive divorce. Think of your boss, how happy he is today.

HENRY: Weasel. My boss is a sneaky weasel.

TRACY: Focus. Deep breaths. Visualize. Food. Clothing. Shelter.

HENRY: I can't.

TRACY: Of course you can. Breathe with me.

(Tracy is too preoccupied to notice KEVIN. Kevin taps her shoulders, taking her by surprise.)

KEVIN: Tracy?

TRACY: Kevin. What are you doing here?

KEVIN: Came to see my dad.

(Kevin waves to Oliver.)

Hi, Dad!

(Oliver waves back.)

TRACY: Of course, how could I forget? I'm such an idiot.

HENRY: Your dad's the President of this Bank?

TRACY: Today's your lucky day, Dad.

HENRY: I can't tell someone you know my problems.

KEVIN: Oh yeah, I heard about your mom. That totally sucks.

TRACY: You know?

KEVIN: If there's anything I can do.

HENRY: Nothing. You can't. Do Anything. We should go. While We Can Still Can.

TRACY: Deep breath. Actually. As long as you know, do you think you could ask your Dad if we could speak to him? Privately.

KEVIN: Sure, I'll grab him.

HENRY: It could be another time.

KEVIN: Or, now.

(Oliver slaps Kevin on the back.)

OLIVER: You lock yourself out of the house again? Run out of money? What brings you here?

KEVIN: Dad, I'd like you to meet Tracy, and her father.

HENRY: Henry.

OLIVER: Enchanté. *(To Tracy:)* Haven't we met before? You look very familiar.

KEVIN: Tracy is the one who beat me last year for best public speaker.

OLIVER: If I remember correctly, that wasn't the only award you won that evening.

KEVIN: She won four awards.

TRACY: Aw shucks, I didn't think anybody noticed.

OLIVER: I certainly noticed. Not everyday your son is a loser in four categories.

HENRY: Did you know four in Mandarin Chinese is a homonym for death?

OLIVER: I'm so sorry, Henry. I thought something was up when I'd see your lovely wife in here, every Friday, like clockwork. But what was I supposed to say? Or, do?

HENRY: Were you two friends?

OLIVER: I tried to engage her in conversation, this is a customer-friendly bank, but she always seemed wrapped up in her own world. A beauty like that, I imagine, needs to fly. I can't, however, imagine the pain you must be going through.

HENRY: Great. Just great, a bank with an overactive imagination.

OLIVER: But I can help you reschedule your mortgage payments so you don't lose your house. If you'll please follow me.

TRACY: Thank you.

(*Tracy follows Henry and Oliver. Kevin follows Tracy.*)

HENRY: Must we do this as a bunch?

OLIVER: (*To Tracy:*) Why don't you stay here and teach my son how to man up?

(*Henry and Oliver exit.*)

TRACY: Does your dad always talk to you like that?

KEVIN: Always. He believes in tough love. Especially for sissies.

TRACY: Why would he think you're a sissy?

KEVIN: Because I was born with a silver spoon in my mouth.

TRACY: Oh, that. Must be nice. Silver.

KEVIN: Plus I want to be a poet.

TRACY: A poet! Are you serious?

KEVIN: Not just any poet. Poet Laureate.

TRACY: Ambitious.

KEVIN: Tough Love says he'll cut me off.

TRACY: Oh dear. What does your mother say?

KEVIN: She drinks.

TRACY: Maybe your parents will come around?

KEVIN: Do you think that we should be allowed to be whatever we want to be?

TRACY: Of course. It's your life; you're the one that has to live it. Own it.

KEVIN: Even if it hurts someone else? Badly?

TRACY: Ouch. Now I know why you're asking me.

KEVIN: I'm asking you because you're so smart. And pretty.

TRACY: Please don't pity me. I know I'm in a bad spot, but pity is so definite and tragic.

KEVIN: Pretty. I said pretty.

TRACY: Oh my god, are you blind? I think you need your eyes checked.

KEVIN: Ouch. The proper response is thank you.

TRACY: Sorry. It's hard to believe I'm good at anything right now. When your mother ups and leaves, it makes you feel like a big fat loser. I may be a whiz at solving differential equations, giving speeches, winning awards, but none of that mattered to my mother.

KEVIN: You know what you need? A break. Dinner and a movie. My treat.

TRACY: I can't. I'm not allowed to date until I'm 21.

KEVIN: That's torture.

TRACY: My father's version of tough love.

KEVIN: What if we "study" together? You heard my dad, he thinks I'm stupid.

TRACY: That's not going to win my father over. Me, spending time with the stupid guy when I need to find a way to get rich quick and save us from the bowels of bankruptcy and depression?

KEVIN: You want to be rich. Rule number one, never take no for an answer.

TRACY: Never?

KEVIN: It's not just what you know, but whom you know.

TRACY: I don't know anyone.

KEVIN: Ergo, you need me. I have access. I have silver spoons.

(Takes out something silver and shiny, sparkles under the lights)

TRACY: Have you ever written a solid business plan?

KEVIN: To be, or not to be. How hard can it be after you've written some poetry? Consider your business plan a poem in free verse.

TRACY: Why do you want to help me? I hope I'm not some charity case you write about in your college essay. I hope I'm not your stepping-stone to Harvard.

KEVIN: Why do you think?

TRACY: I try not to think about boys. It helps me crush the competition and land straight A's.

KEVIN: Well, that's simply unacceptable going forward. Not if you want to become rich. Old *Boys* Club.

TRACY: Ever notice the people who say money isn't everything are usually people that don't have any?

KEVIN: Same people who say, "Everything happens for a reason."

TRACY: Money can't buy happiness. Are these people just plain stupid?

KEVIN: It's an honor just to be nominated. *("L" over forehead:)* Loser.

TRACY: Cheer up, things always turn out for the best. Yeah right. My mother's leaving us is the best thing that happened to me. I hate it when someone says that to me.

KEVIN: Oh, for sure, hardship builds character. Fiber. Because it's the journey, not the destination.

TRACY: Because winning isn't everything.

TRACY/KEVIN: Losers. Capital L.

KEVIN: Not like us.

TRACY: No way, the two of us are definitely going somewhere. To the mountaintop.

KEVIN: To the moon.

TRACY: My dreams have always been Scary Ginormous. Before my mother left us, I had no reason to limit myself. So I didn't. But, now. To think I could be the next Steve Jobs or Oprah Winfrey *now* when I don't even have a mother who loves me. When we might lose our house. Now I'll be lucky if I can even afford to go to college. Reality check, downsize, downsize, downsize.

KEVIN: Supersize. That's what rich people do.

TRACY: You're right. When the market goes south, you don't flee, you stock up. Buy more.

KEVIN: Dinner and a brainstorm? My treat.

TRACY: You're on. What good is a dream that cannot stop the rain and hold up the heavens above?

KEVIN: Indeed. Supersize those dreams.

(Kevin gives Tracy a quick kiss when no one's looking. So quick, and awkward, Tracy thinks it was an accident. Both too embarrassed to own up to it. Blackout to see a night sky.)

(End of Scene 4.)

SCENE 5

(Miss Nutter's office, Kucinich High School. Tracy is texting Kevin as she waits for Miss Nutter. Tracy giggles, engrossed.)

MISS NUTTER: And here I was worried I kept you waiting too long. Can't tell you how happy it makes me to hear you giggle. Giggle away, my friend.

TRACY: Me, giggle? I beg to differ.

MISS NUTTER: A woman should never lose her giggle. According to my mom. Oh, I'm so sorry, how insensitive of me.

TRACY: Stop. I'm going to have to get used to it. Mother's Day is going to be a train wreck. I can already see it coming. Fleets of loving mothers and daughters.

MISS NUTTER: I wasn't thinking, such an idiot.

TRACY: Most people have moms.

MISS NUTTER: Yes, that's true.

TRACY: I wish I had one. But I have drive. Zoom, zoom.

MISS NUTTER: You have gifts.

TRACY: You keep saying, and I keep believing, I have to, but there's only one way to find out. I need to put myself out there. On the hiring and firing line.

MISS NUTTER: You can do anything you put your mind to.

TRACY: So you'll help me get half the day off. Talk to Principal Healy.

MISS NUTTER: Cut school?

TRACY: The pros of being an overachiever, finished my AP classes early. The cons, my afternoons are largely wasted.

"Study" halls. And Kevin told me there's this thing called Independent Study reserved for very special students.

MISS NUTTER: Kevin Wilcox?

TRACY: Yes.

MISS NUTTER: Since when are you and Kevin Wilcox friends?

TRACY: Since we ran into each other at the bank? We were also rivals in Junior Achievement.

MISS NUTTER: Is that who you were texting earlier?

TRACY: He told me his Uncle Dave used to get out early to take classes at Kent State. So why can't I get out early to work?

MISS NUTTER: What kind of work?

TRACY: Not sure yet, but I do have a few very important interviews lined up. Wish me luck.

MISS NUTTER: What? When? Details.

TRACY: I queried some CEOs. Mostly by email. Followed up by a phone call.

MISS NUTTER: CEOs as in Chief Executive Officers?

TRACY: I know, I can't believe it either. But I read when Steve Jobs was in high school and needed a job, he called the President of HP. Can you imagine? The President of Hewlett-Packard. Always aim for the top. So I aimed. For the top. You know you're always saying I'm an excellent writer? Apparently, I am. That's how I've been landing my interviews. One CEO said I write the best cover letters, and he has to meet me.

MISS NUTTER: This sounds way over your head, I don't approve. Has to meet you? No. Cross him off your list.

TRACY: No worries, he thinks I'm an adult.

MISS NUTTER: But you're not.

TRACY: But you said I could do anything I set my mind to, anything. Was that just that gooey marshmallow fluff?

MISS NUTTER: No, of course not. I say what I mean.

TRACY: Then please you're going to mean what you say when you praise me to the Seven Hills when I list you as a reference. And you can't mention my age. Ever. Not even the slightest clue.

MISS NUTTER: I don't know.

TRACY: Age discrimination is illegal. You can't break the law!

MISS NUTTER: What about college? I hate to see you give up the Ivy League. Miss out on the opportunity of a lifetime.

TRACY: Don't you see? If we lose our house, there will be no college, no lifetime.

MISS NUTTER: What is your father doing? Ultimately it's his responsibility.

TRACY: You saw him. Brokenhearted. Defeated. He's in no shape. The sirens are blaring. What choice do I have?

MISS NUTTER: Promise me you'll keep me posted and turn to me if anything, and I mean anything, goes awry.

TRACY: No doubt, if you do this for me, I will be forever indebted.

MISS NUTTER: You are so very brave. And such courage should be rewarded with a book. Not just any book. But a first edition for a first-class student.

(Hands Tracy a book:)

TRACY: *The Great Gatsby?* First edition, I can't accept.

MISS NUTTER: Just promise me you won't sell it.

TRACY: Keep it. Already read it.

MISS NUTTER: Read it again, and again, until you know it by heart, cover-to-cover, line by line.

TRACY: Why?

MISS NUTTER: Words matter. Words have magical healing powers. *(Writes an inscription to Tracy on cover page:)* To Tracy, who is very brave.

TRACY: Stop it, what makes me so brave?

MISS NUTTER: You believe in the green light. You see the green light.

TRACY: And tomorrow, I will run faster, stretch my arms out farther -

MISS NUTTER: And one fine morning –

TRACY: And then what? My mother leaves, my father falls into an abyss, Alex cuts school, and I roll over, and die?

MISS NUTTER: Your courage kicks in and propels you. To the edge of the pier. To a new beginning.

(End of Scene 5.)

SCENE 6

(Tracy's home. Kevin has selected several wardrobe options for Tracy's big job interview.)

TRACY: Sorry I'm running late. You know Miss Nutter. She means well, but she thinks books are the answers to everything.

KEVIN: For every problem, there is a book. A story. At least one, if not ten. That you must read cover to cover, memorize every line, and recite in a crowded room to distinguish yourself from the uninspired.

TRACY: She prescribed *Great Gatsby* by F. Scott. He was such a dreamer.

KEVIN: And an alcoholic.

TRACY: We all need a support system.

KEVIN: So, these are my top wardrobe recommendations. Dress the part. Older.

TRACY: Wiser.

KEVIN: Richer. Your mother owned a Chanel. Did you know that? I thought you were poor. Look at the tags.

TRACY: Chanel! How could she do that to us? Spend money we didn't have. She was such a clotheshorse. My father hated that about her. She wanted to be rich, look rich. Like me. I'm going to turn out just like her, aren't I? Like mother, like daughter.

KEVIN: Earth to Tracy. You need to focus. Get in the zone.

TRACY: We should return this. Help me find the receipt. *(Looks in pocket:)* Oh my god, it's my graduation present. "For Tracy, Happy Graduation."

KEVIN: You can't return your mother's last gift. You're wearing this.

TRACY: I'm not sure I'm worth this. Happy Graduation. That's all she can say? Where's "Love, Mom?"

KEVIN: You're worth more. A lot more.

TRACY: I don't want to look too rich, like I don't need a job. Or, a family.

KEVIN: Or too old because statistics show employers prefer young and fresh. High energy.

TRACY: But not too young that I look like I'm still in high school.

KEVIN: Or too much like a man that seems to repel employers across the board. Being something you're not.

TRACY: The question that torments women everywhere. What to Wear. What Not to Wear.

KEVIN: You're lucky your mother was such a fashionista, and couldn't take it with her. Gives you plenty of stylish options.

TRACY: How could she forget to sign the note, "Love, Mom"?

KEVIN: She was probably in too much of a rush.

TRACY: I don't feel too well. I want to lie down.

KEVIN: No. This is your future. You need to reach for the sky. Stretch.

TRACY: You're right. Times like this, I have to dig deep and ask myself, What Would Oprah Wear?

(End of Scene 6.)

SCENE 7

(Diner. Tracy eats voraciously during her job interview with CHRISTOPHER BRENNAN.)

CHRISTOPHER: Wow, you sure can eat. I've never seen a woman eat with such wild abandon. And you look like you're really enjoying the food too. You're not just bingeing.

TRACY: Oh, I guess I should have eaten breakfast. *(Puts her fork down:)* But I hate breakfast. I find the choices too limiting.

CHRISTOPHER: I can see why. Cheeseburger. Fries. Clam Chowder. Salad. Unsweetened ice tea. Not exactly breakfast foods. You know, early in my career, I had to decide, do I gnaw on the chicken bone, or do I want that job?

TRACY: Sorry. I just assumed we'd talk about the job after we ate.

CHRISTOPHER: Don't apologize. I love a woman with a voracious appetite.

TRACY: You do?

CHRISTOPHER: I hate it when I take my date out to a five star restaurant and all she wants is a tiny garden salad. Makes me furious.

TRACY: Oh I'd never do that.

CHRISTOPHER: I don't suppose it's in your DNA.

TRACY: Not yet. Maybe I'll mutate when I'm older. I'm told it happens.

CHRISTOPHER: People with voracious appetites make the best employees. They're hungry. And if they eat in front of you, you know they're honest. As opposed to those critters who eat a salad in front of you and when you're not looking, raid the entire refrigerator.

TRACY: Well, in that case, don't mind if I take another big, delicious bite.

CHRISTOPHER: You must work out. To eat like a teenager.

TRACY: Oh. Yes. I have very high metabolism. Plus I ride my bike everywhere.

CHRISTOPHER: Hard-core environmentalist.

TRACY: Could be, someday.

CHRISTOPHER: So, I looked over your resume. Very impressive.

TRACY: Thank you.

CHRISTOPHER: Watching you eat, however, makes me wonder, why did you fold your Chinese dumpling business? Seems to me, food is your passion.

TRACY: Food is so labor intensive. Not that I'm afraid of work. I'm not. But I was tired of smelling of dough, egg-wash, ginger and soy sauce 24/7.

CHRISTOPHER: Sounds sublime to me. Cleveland is not known for its winning Chinese cuisine.

TRACY: Believe me, I know. My father's number one complaint.

CHRISTOPHER: The other thing is, did you go to college?

TRACY: Steve Jobs, Michael Dell, Bill Gates, they all dropped out.

CHRISTOPHER: So you're a college dropout.

TRACY: No. Not exactly. I did take a math class at Kent State once. I want to study more, but my father, he's not well, and...

(*Tracy starts to tremble, voice falters.*)

CHRISTOPHER: I'm so sorry.

TRACY: Me too, me too.   It's imperative I step up and sacrifice.

CHRISTOPHER: Yes, it all makes sense now.

TRACY: I still want to. Some day. But not everyone needs to graduate from college to be successful, right? Look at you. You dropped out of Stanford.

CHRISTOPHER: You've done your homework.

TRACY: I excel at homework. Homework is my favorite subject.

CHRISTOPHER: So why do you want to work for me?

TRACY: Like me, you have something to prove. And I can get you there.

CHRISTOPHER: This sounds very interesting.

TRACY: Every time you start something new, it turns to gold. But then your investors, your shareholders they all say your management style sucks. You're too mercurial, unable to trust and delegate, you shoot your best people down, causing a divide as vast as the Grand Canyon.

CHRISTOPHER: Harsh.

TRACY: Sensing a lucrative opportunity, corporate raiders like Duke Manning swoop in and hostile take-over. You're through. Ejected. Bird doo.

CHRISTOPHER: Anyone ever tell you maybe you should get out there more, live a little, and screw homework?

TRACY: Uh, no.

CHRISTOPHER: And why should I trust you who comes forth with slings and arrows?

TRACY: I'm going to share some of my new ideas with you, and I'm going to offer to work for you for two weeks free. If you don't like what I do, no obligation. But if you do like what I have to offer, you make me an offer I can't refuse. Deal?

CHRISTOPHER: Let's see some of these new ideas you have.

(Tracy pulls out her computer bag. It's not her computer. It's Kevin's computer and stuff.)

TRACY: Oh my god. This computer. It's not—

CHRISTOPHER: What's wrong?

(Kevin races over. He snuck in earlier and hid.)

KEVIN: Miss, I believe this is yours.

TRACY: *(Relieved:)* Of course. We must have switched at the...at the...

KEVIN: Bank. I followed you when I realized, I didn't want to interrupt, but –

TRACY: Thank you. I'm so sorry.

KEVIN: It's not your fault. They all look alike.

TRACY: They do, don't they?

KEVIN: Well, I better let you get back to whatever.

CHRISTOPHER: Yes. Please. This young woman promised to rock my world.

(Kevin leaves.)

TRACY: The first thing we need to make is computer bags. They shouldn't all look alike. Big, black, clunky. Every "geek" deserves some style.

CHRISTOPHER: Especially geeks. Was this a complete setup?

TRACY: *(Giggles:)* Let's see what happens when we go online and shop for computer bags. Same, same, same.

CHRISTOPHER: Brilliant.

TRACY: I also designed our new company logo.

CHRISTOPHER: You're kidding. Whatever possessed you to undertake this task?

TRACY: Did you know Carolyn Knight was a student at Portland State when she designed the Nike Swoosh? She was given 35 dollars and 500 shares of stock.

CHRISTOPHER: I suppose this means you'd like to also be paid in stock.

TRACY: Oh, could I?

CHRISTOPHER: Well, don't keep a mogul waiting, let's see what you got.

TRACY: Thought you'd never ask. Exhibit A.

(OVERHEAD PROJECTION of "ADVANCE, INC." in different logos, fonts, colors, styles, graphic designs.)

(ADVANCE	*ADVANCE)*
(ADVANCE	*ADVANCE)*
(ADVANCE	*ADVANCE)*
(ADVANCE	*ADVANCE)*
(ADVANCE	*ADVANCE)*
(ADVANCE	*ADVANCE)*
(ADVANCE	*ADVANCE)*

TRACY: Steve Jobs started out in calligraphy and changed the world. Think of what we can do. It's our turn.

CHRISTOPHER: Really. Such a go-getter. You said ideas plural.

TRACY: *(Pulls out some Chinese silk fabrics with gold threads, blues, reds, yellows, gold silver:)* Rub these against your face. Think about what it might like to be to sleep on these luxurious silks that come in vibrant colors. With gold threads. Dragons and phoenixes. Flowers.

CHRISTOPHER: Luxury high-end bedding. Nice and soft. You're hired. When can you start?

TRACY: Tomorrow too soon?

CHRISTOPHER: Bright and early.

TRACY: Actually I need some flexibility.

CHRISTOPHER: There's always a catch. What are you, on parole?

TRACY: In the morning, I need to...need to...

CHRISTOPHER: Take care of your dad. I get it.

TRACY: I can always be there after twelve noon. But in the mornings, I need to telecommute.

CHRISTOPHER: Fine. How much do you want?

TRACY: As in money?

CHRISTOPHER: Don't waffle now. Bring on the "homework."

TRACY: A hundred grand? With performance-based stock options, and a signing bonus of ten grand.

CHRISTOPHER: Signing bonus! You were going to give me two weeks free.

TRACY: But I just realized I already did so much homework. Pretty please?

CHRISTOPHER: Done.   How's Director of Marketing Research sound?

TRACY: You won't regret this.

CHRISTOPHER: I better not.   Or I'll sue for damages. Kidding. Or, not.

   (*End of Scene 7.*)

SCENE 8

(Marina's home. There's a "Foreclosure Sale" sign on the front lawn. The house has been vandalized. Tracy knocks on Marina's door. Marina answers.)

MARINA: In case you missed all the "signs," we're not buying anything.

TRACY: I'm really sorry about your father.

MARINA: Why do you care? We were never friends.

TRACY: I think you're really talented.

MARINA: Sorry we got kicked out of the country club?

TRACY: Not so much. But I was told I'm not exactly country club material.

MARINA: You're not. *(Beat.)* But neither am I. Not anymore. Apparently.

(Tracy and Marina share a laugh.)

So why are you here?

TRACY: Business proposition. The downside, long hours. Upside, performance-based stock options.

MARINA: Stock options! My father lost everybody's money in the stock market.

TRACY: I know. But he also made people a lot of money, right?

MARINA: Everybody sure loved him then. People forget investments are a risk. It says so in the fine print.

TRACY: Here's your chance. Chance of a lifetime. Chance to make it big. Chance sounds so much more enchanting than risk, doesn't it?

MARINA: Very much so. And safer. Confident. Self-assured.

TRACY: And yet, there are no guarantees in life.

MARINA: Do you believe my father's innocent? The truth.

TRACY: I honestly don't know. I don't know enough. Sorry.

MARINA: I suppose that's fair. We weren't exactly friends. More like frenemies.

TRACY: Please, Marina. Truth, you hated me.

MARINA: You were such a goody-goody-two shoe overachiever. How could anyone compete? You should've gotten a "D" every now and then. Then I would've liked you.

TRACY: Even when you think it's safe to do nothing, it's a risk. Even when day after day, you do your best, your absolute best to make someone proud, make someone love you, one day you go home, and it's gone. Your mother's stopped. Loving. You.

MARINA: One day, you're belle of the ball, homecoming queen, and the envy spans all the way to the Brooklyn Bridge, and the next day, you find out your father is being sued for fraud and total strangers want to spit on you. And do.

TRACY: The money you thought was earmarked for college–

MARINA: Or starting your own design firm–

TRACY/MARINA: Kaput. Gone.

MARINA: Stock options, huh? What company?

TRACY: Our company. Banking on us.

MARINA: You're putting a lot of faith in someone that hated your guts.

TRACY: It is definitely a risk.

MARINA: Or, a "chance of a lifetime."

TRACY: I'm enchanted, aren't you? What have we got to lose? I don't want to die like this, do you?

MARINA: Would this make you my boss?

TRACY: It would.

MARINA: What am I designing?

TRACY: Style for geeks.

(Tracy models her plain black computer bag)

MARINA: How stylish. Not. I wouldn't be seen with a geek.

TRACY: Even more reason to give that geek some style. Even geeks deserve some style and respect, especially when we rule the world, don't you think?

MARINA: I'm not especially fond of geeks. Few people are.

TRACY: We can change all that. You can change all that.

MARINA: Give me the fine print.

TRACY: Besides being your...shush...underage boss and hiring someone whose father may be headed for prison? It's quite scandalous as is, don't you think?

MARINA: Oh my god, you're one those annoying prodigies who skipped a grade–

TRACY: Or two.

MARINA: So, the worst thing that can happen is...we lose our house?

TRACY: We lose sight of our future.

MARINA: I can see now how some of us need to take more chances than others.

TRACY: Even if you turn me down, swear to me you'll carry this secret to the grave. Honor code.

MARINA: I swear I'm no rat. A jury could very well find my father guilty. Condemn him as a white-collar criminal. The evidence is rather overwhelmingly against him.

TRACY: We are not responsible for our parents' actions. I tell this to myself every morning so I can get out of bed.

MARINA: Did you get that from a book?

TRACY: (*Chuckles:*) Actually, I did.

MARINA: Why should we put ourselves on the line? Why is it our responsibility to save our parents? Our selves?

TRACY: It's either go big, or go home, and which one of us wants to go home? What home?

(*End of Act I.*)

ACT II

SCENE 1

(TV. Local news. RITA STOREY interviews Christopher on the local news. Tracy, Alex, Kevin, Marina, DUKE are watching from several vantage points [wings, audience, side].)

RITA: Well-known fact, Ohio is the mother of Presidents, and serial killers. A dubious distinction, and one that's aroused much speculation on a possible correlation, being the serial killer capitol of the world, and producing the most U.S. Presidents, but if CEO Christopher Brennan has his way, the Buckeye State will soon be known for innovation and entrepreneurship. Christopher, with raging unemployment, and record foreclosures, what on earth possessed you to reinvent yourself and launch Advance, Incorporated in Cleveland, Ohio?

CHRISTOPHER: Sheer stupidity and pride.

RITA: What, stupidity and pride go together like peanut butter and jelly?

CHRISTOPHER: Look, it's never a good time to put yourself out on a limb. Life is a gamble. The odds are always against you. You could cross the street and get hit by a semi.

RITA: Such an optimist. Then again, you did return to Ohio with your tail tucked between your legs.

CHRISTOPHER: Sweet, Rita. Last I checked, we lost our tails to evolution.

RITA: Some of your former employees think the reason you retreated to Ohio is you couldn't face running into Duke Manning again. That essentially you're in hiding, because Duke Manning would never expect you to succeed here.

CHRISTOPHER: Midwesterners get no respect.   Especially Buckeyes.   Ever notice in film and TV, the naïve waif, the moron, the poor unsuspecting victim—

RITA: Or serial killer.

CHRISTOPHER: Is always from Ohio.

RITA: Aha! You are here to make a statement.

CHRISTOPHER: Cleveland Rocks. Buckeyes Buck. Bucking Rock, Buckeyes.

RITA: Your new mantra. Bucking Rock. How profane.

CHRISTOPHER: Six months ago, I thought I lost it all. Duke Manning had just bought my third company and once again convinced the board to oust me.

RITA: Third time's the charm. Duke Manning said it was like gravy. Icing on a cake.

CHRISTOPHER: Returned home to find my father can't remember my name, or who I am.

RITA: Lost your father, your company, your girlfriend. A trifecta.

CHRISTOPHER: Funny thing how most people are not attracted to nosey reporters, or to losers.

RITA: Oh, Christopher, nothing you can say can keep Rita Storey away.

CHRISTOPHER: Can't blame me for trying. I Bucking Rock.

RITA: Is that why you've launched another business? You can't help yourself.   "Obsessive compulsive manufacturing disorder." What made you think of redesigning the computer bag and launching a product line for geeks? And your use of social media, and "found" objects, how very progressive. Youthful. Radiant Green.

CHRISTOPHER: New product development is where it's at. If you keep reinvesting the money in developing new products, you can keep the corporate raiders at bay. Hear that, Duke, don't bother robbing us. We're creating real value.

RITA: It's like you're a new man. Reborn. Kinder, gentler CEO.

(Rita shows off some computer bags.)

CHRISTOPHER: I met someone special. Very special. Who believes in me, and helped me renew my faith. Grow.

RITA: Oh, do tell. Name. Rank. File. I live for these precious sparkling gems.

CHRISTOPHER: She's pretty shy. Prefers to stay behind the scenes. Out of the limelight. So she can think. Focus. Work.

RITA: She must be brilliant.

CHRISTOPHER: A diamond.

RITA: When do I get to meet her?

CHRISTOPHER: You don't. I'd just feel like a narcissist if I took all the credit. She said I could, and should, but I can't. That would be bad karma.

RITA: Everybody knows how Rita Storey feels about secrets.

CHRISTOPHER: Please, Rita, do what's right for Cleveland. For Ohio. Bucking Rock, Buckeye.

RITA: Of course, of course, you know me.

(Rita's cell phone RINGS.)

Oops, excuse me, I have to take this.

CHRISTOPHER: Reporters, always on. Take it, and Buck, Rita. Buck.

DUKE MANNING: *(Voice:)* I want that mystery woman. Find her. Get me a date with destiny.

(End of Scene 1.)

SCENE 2

(Stuffy upscale restaurant. Tracy enters to meet Duke Manning for dinner.)

TRACY: I really don't understand why we couldn't meet for lunch.

DUKE: Well, nice to meet you, too.

TRACY: Sorry, it's just that I'm so busy.

DUKE: Exactly. How would either of us get enough work done before and after lunch?

TRACY: This feels so extravagant. What is it you want?

DUKE: Very direct, I like that. I flew in from Texas to see you. The real you, not the rushed you. Aren't you going to give me some Oh-Hi-Oh? You and Christopher make it sound like it's such a friendly state.

TRACY: Texas. Oh hi oh, Duke, but I'm not sure I'm worth the airfare.

DUKE: Corporate jet. You're lucky I didn't force you and Christopher to come visit me on my ranch. You'd love my Kobe beef. It's fresh if you know what I mean.

TRACY: You can do that? Force me to go to Texas?

DUKE: You ever had Kobe beef? I feed my cows sake and beer mash, and they get daily massages so that marbled beef melts on your tongue. Like butter.

TRACY: I'm famished. And at these prices, it's no wonder why.

DUKE: Order whatever you want. My treat.

TRACY: Even the Kobe beef?

DUKE: I'd be especially honored. It's my meat.

TRACY: Figures. No wonder you're rich.

DUKE: You say it like that's a bad thing.

TRACY: Oh no. Can't hate the rich if I want to be the rich.

DUKE: Amen. How about a big bold smooth bottle of French red to celebrate? Goes well with Kobe beef.

TRACY: Thanks, feel free, but I can't drink.

DUKE: Oh yes you can. You're like me, you can do anything you set your mind or heart or lips to. That's why I want to hire you.

TRACY: Me? You're crazy.

DUKE: Truth be told, I prefer irascible. I brought you a cowboy hat. Us two, we're mavericks.

TRACY: You act like you know me.

DUKE: I know everything I need to know.

TRACY: Oh no you don't. I promise you that.

DUKE: Really. Is that a threat?

TRACY: I'm just saying.

DUKE: If you're as sharp as I think you are, you know Duke Manning never backs down from a challenge.

TRACY: Sounds more like you're threatening me.

DUKE: If you turn me down, I'll just have to buy the company. So we can do this the easy way, or the hard way.

TRACY: Are you kidding me?

DUKE: Duke Manning always gets what he wants. Sooner, or later. Usually sooner.

TRACY: Why do you want me so much? You and Christopher have this sick macho rivalry where you like to take away whatever he has to prove your...hat's bigger than his hat? Instead of buying up other people's hard work and shattering their dreams, why don't you invent or create something from scratch for a change?

DUKE: Miss Tracy! Don't be insulting your new boss. That isn't exactly a career-builder.

TRACY: I can't work for you.

DUKE: I'll pay you double.

TRACY: Double?

DUKE: Why settle for rich when you can be twice as rich?

TRACY: Could I get a signing bonus?

DUKE: See. What did I tell you? You and me, two peas in a pod. How much?

TRACY: I can't move. Cross state lines.

DUKE: Sure you can. Everything comes with a price. How much?

(Rita Storey has snuck in and snaps photograph after photograph.)

RITA: Yes, how much would it take? Details, details. Rita Storey and *The Wall Street Journal* want to know.

TRACY: What are you doing here?

RITA: Working. So for the record, are you officially joining Manning Enterprises?

TRACY: Get out. Security!

RITA: Manners! Public place. Anything you say can be held against you.

TRACY: You can't publish these photographs.

RITA: Watch me. Extra, extra! Read all about it.

(Rita keeps snapping away. Tracy blocks her face.)

TRACY: I'm calling 9-1-1.

RITA: To say what, a reporter crashed your dinner party? Don't be juvenile.

TRACY: Duke, you've got to stop her. Please. You said you could do anything.

RITA: Who do you think tipped me off, sweetheart? Thanks, Duke. As we speak, stock of Advance, Incorporated is going up, up, up. Buy, buy, buy.

TRACY: How could you?

DUKE: She helped me find you. That was the deal.

TRACY: Great. Just for the record, I could never work for you. Never.

RITA: Ouch. Tomorrow's banner headline, Texas Mogul Duke Manning is rejected. Wham Bam.

TRACY: And as for you, Rita...

RITA: Bring it on, make it bleed rare and juicy.

TRACY: I think I'm having a heart attack. I haven't felt this sick since my mother left.

DUKE: Miss Tracy. What's come over you? What is it you're so afraid of?

(End of Scene 2.)

SCENE 3

(Ballroom, Four Seasons, Annual Shareholders Meeting. APPPLAUSE. Christopher has just finished his annual address to SHAREHOLDERS. Also seated: Tracy, Rita, Marina. Duke Manning rises and approaches podium.)

DUKE: Ladies and Gentlemen, let us take another moment to thank Christopher Brennan for Rocking Bucking Buckeye. Christopher Brennan has no equal when it comes to knowing how to ignite a dream. I say that from the bottom of my heart, not just the bottom of my wallet. Everyone has his or her forte. Your skin breaks out, you call a dermatologist. You need braces, you visit an orthodontist. High blood pressure, heart murmurs, you call a cardiologist. As a protector of shareholder value and yes, a majority shareholder, I know you can't always see or predict what's up ahead. You can, however, put yourself in the most capable hands, hearts and minds you find. Business is like medicine; early prevention and early detection are key to vibrancy and prolonged life. Change forces us to reinvent and redefine ourselves to survive. I know it takes a team, a company, a village to evolve and succeed, but there's one person who has been the force of driving change. One person with exceptional vision. One person who deserves special recognition. One person who embodies the Great American Dream. And that person is Miss Tracy. As the patron saint of shareholder value, I strongly urge each and every one of you vote to remove Christopher Brennan as CEO and replace him with Miss Tracy. For my money, Miss Tracy is the right woman to lead us into the promised future.

(GASPS. MAYHEM.)

CHRISTOPHER: *(To Tracy:)* I trusted you, you backstabbing conniving ungrateful witch —

TRACY: Stop! I'm just as surprised as you are.

CHRISTOPHER: And I was born yesterday.

DUKE: He can't hurt you now, Miss Tracy. He's over. Past. Whatever was holding you back, no more.

CHRISTOPHER: You've been acting all bizarre ever since your cozy rendezvous was splashed all over the news. You don't think I've noticed? You think I'm blind?

RITA: Details.

TRACY: If I was acting strange, it's because you can all hurt me.

CHRISTOPHER: It's like Duke flipped your switch.

RITA: Ominous. Not unlike a serial killer about to go off.

TRACY: Oh, very unlike.

MARINA: Don't listen to her; her job is to provoke you.

CHRISTOPHER: Almost like you're in a witness protection program.

TRACY: You have to admit ever since Duke staked his claim, we've been under an awful lot of pressure. Public scrutiny.

MARINA: Tracy's is one of those round pegs in a square peg world.

DUKE: Perfect. Let's vote.

MARINA: Tracy, you and me, haven't we suffered enough? Our stock prices are through the roof! Sell first. You can always quit.

DUKE: Quit? Quitters get no respect in my book.

CHRISTOPHER: No mercy.

HENRY: Do not bring shame or poverty unto your family. You promised. Where is the stock now?

MARINA: Seventy-eight. This job means everything to me.

HENRY: Seventy-eight!

RITA: I smell sizzling high steaks. Manna from heaven.

TRACY: I tell myself other people have mothers, but I have director of marketing research. Other people drive sports cars, I have drive. Other people wear designer jeans, we design. If I lose this, I have nothing. Nothing.

DUKE: What's all this loser talk, Miss Tracy? It's a slam-dunk. Watch. All in favor of voting Miss Tracy as CEO, say "Aye."

ALL SHAREHOLDERS: *(Minus Christopher, Minus Tracy:)* Aye.

TRACY: Sorry, I can't.

DUKE: Can.

MARINA: Can.

HENRY: Can. But it's up to you. What do I know?

TRACY: Make no mistake. I do want to be CEO of a major corporation someday, and break all kinds of records. I do. But, I'm sixteen. And unlicensed to drive by the DMV.

(GASPS.)

RITA: Sixteen and unlicensed! How did this happen?

CHRISTOPHER: You're going to pay. For all the shareholders.

DUKE: Duke Manning is nobody's jackass.

MARINA: Oh please. It's not like she made a sex tape, or butchered small animals into nibbly bits. Get real. We both worked our butts off. Made everybody a lot of money, or why are we standing here?

RITA: Your designer Marina has a valid point, and jagged edge. How do you respond?

DUKE: Talk to my lawyer.

HENRY: It's all my fault. After my wife of 17 years left, I fell into a bottomless black hole.

TRACY: You don't have to explain, Dad. It's all my fault. Sheer stupidity and pride. Ring a bell, Christopher?

CHRISTOPHER: This man's your father? He doesn't look ill to me.

HENRY: I'm sick on the inside. Tracy only did what she did to save the house, the family. Me. We were on the verge of bankruptcy.

MARINA: She saved me too. Gave me something to live for.

CHRISTOPHER: Spare me. You're both fired.

RITA: The hostile takeover still on, Duke?

DUKE: Do I strike you as certifiably crazy? Hell no. I'm going to start an internal investigation.

RITA: So Christopher gets to keep his company, Advance, Incorporated.

DUKE: Yes, for what it's worth. Which could be nothing.

RITA: Congratulations, Christopher, you finally beat Duke Manning! How will you celebrate? Will you invite and re-hire Marina and Tracy? Or, will you let that stock price hit rock bottom?

MARINA: *(To Christopher:)* You should be thanking Tracy. She gave you a gift no one has been able to give you. Not even yourself. Merry freaking Christmas.

RITA: Feisty. May I see some form of ID showing proof of age?

TRACY: Christopher, you promised if I helped you keep your company, you'd help me, you said you'd owe me— *(She pulls out Christopher's writing:)* I could've sold the stock, pulled out, made a killing,

MARINA: We all could've made a killing, but you promised.

TRACY: If you break your word, Christopher, we're going to lose the house.

RITA: Touching, is that true? May I see that document?

CHRISTOPHER: *(Grabs and tears it up:)* Considering you're a freaking minor, and committed fraud, that contract written under duress is hereby null and void.

TRACY: You never asked me my age. You just assumed, and I let you assume because I was desperate after my mother abandoned us. We wanted to live. To thrive.

CHRISTOPHER: Dead to me.

RITA: Your stock is now trading below 50. And dropping.

(Marina grabs Tracy.)

MARINA: Let's pray. To our patron saint, Steve Jobs.

MARINA/TRACY: *(Mixture of trading off lines, and overlapping:)* "Here's to the crazy ones. The misfits. The rebels. The troublemakers. The round pegs in the square holes. The ones who see things differently. They're not fond of rules and they have no respect for the status-quo. You can quote them, disagree with them, glorify, or vilify them. But the only thing you can't do is ignore them. Because they change things. They push the human race forward. And while some may see them as the crazy ones, we see genius. Because the people who are crazy enough to think they can change the world, are the ones who do."

(End of Scene 3.)

SCENE 4

(Internet [surfing] and Tracy's home. For Sale sign. Tracy is depressed, her friends and family intervene. Various responses to Tracy's "transgression." Headlines should be projected on a screen, or on stage. Videos can be performed live, or be taped videos.)

HENRY: Cheer up; you're headed to college soon. It's not like you were going to live here forever.

ALEX: Seriously I'm the one that's going to suffer. Not only do I have to move, but now people are going to ask me, why can't you be more like your sister? I am my own man.

HENRY: A house is just a house, but it takes us to make a home.

KEVIN: *(Surfing the Internet:)* There's already a bidding war on your house. Rumor has it this house has really good feng-shui. Killer feng-shui.

HENRY: The money house. Cha-ching cha-ching! Buy low, sell high!

ALEX: We're all over the Internet! You're famous.

(Headline: "TEEN THWARTS HOSTILE TAKEOVER":)

MALE TEEN ON VIDEO: *(Playing guitar:)* Oh, Tracy, Oh Tracy, you bring home the bacon, and I'll supply the melody, together we'll make perfect harmony.

KEVIN: *(Jealous, clicks off:)* Do you know that guy? He needs a good haircut.

TRACY: 'Course not.

HENRY: Thank God.

KEVIN: So you like me.

HENRY: You'll do.

KEVIN: Hear that, Tracy? It's official. Your father likes me.

HENRY: Next.

COUPLE ON VIDEO: Our son is thirty-four and still living at home. He doesn't give us a cent and we can't kick him out. Whose fault is that?

(*The couple point to each other.*)

Too permissive. Tracy, can you train and motivate our son?

HENRY: Ask 'em how much.

MARINA: Once the dust settles, you're going to get a lot of job offers. Just remember to take me with you!

(*Headline   2,   "GIRL   WUNDERKIND   DUPES   TWO MOGULS":*)

COMPANY OWNER ON VIDEO 2: What's the big deal? Mozart began composing at age five. Andrew Carnegie started work at thirteen. Bobby Fischer stunned the world when he became a grandmaster of chess at fifteen. I could use another hard worker. Tracy, you want to strut your stuff, come work here any time. We can even car pool.

ALEX: Notice how he failed to mention what kind of company. Sweat shop!

(*Headline 3, "ALIEN INVADES FORTUNE 500, NO OUTER LIMITS:"*)

TRACY: Alien! That bites. I'm an American citizen!

ALEX: At least they didn't call you a terrorist.

TRACY: I don't understand. If I'm all over the Internet, why hasn't my mother reached out?

HENRY: Is that why you're glued to your computer?

TRACY: All this notoriety, all this heartbreak out there, and nothing. Am I that unlovable?

EVERYONE: No.

KEVIN: The class voted you Most Likely To Bounce.

TRACY: I've never bounced a check in my life.

KEVIN: It's for your resilience. Your ability to bounce back, silly.

TRACY: Why doesn't my mother love me?

(No one can answer so they click on another page.)

KEVIN: Oh, look.

(Headline 4, "TEEN CRASHES MARKET AND KILLS DREAMS:")

TRACY: Turn it off. No wonder, my mother can't love me. I killed my mother's dreams.

HENRY: No, Tracy. That's how I felt too. I blamed myself. Didn't buy enough gifts, wasn't romantic enough, couldn't cook. A lot of things wrong with me. And a lot of things wrong with your mother. Sorry to say.

MARINA: I used to blame myself too, and like maybe if I didn't have such expensive tastes, maybe if I had cheaper dreams…maybe my father wouldn't have been so greedy. But you know what you told me? You are not responsible for what your parents did to you, but you are responsible for taking positive steps towards securing a better future.

TRACY: Yeah, look how well that turned out. Some future. We're going to be homeless. Save the last cardboard box for me.

HENRY: It turned out great.

ALEX: So we're not rich, we have each other. And our health.

TRACY: That bad.

KEVIN: You have me.

MISS NUTTER: You've been accepted to every college you applied for.

TRACY: We should have sold the stock. What was I thinking?

MISS NUTTER: That you were a good person. Too good. Like Gatsby.

MARINA: You should have ousted Christopher.

ALEX: Moved to Texas and worked for Duke.

HENRY: But you didn't do any of these things, why?

TRACY: Because I'm the biggest loser! Lord Jim! Going down with the ship.

HENRY: Because you have character. You know what happens to people with character?

TRACY: They burn in Hell for eternity.

HENRY: It means wherever you go, you're going to shine like a superstar. People can always find superstars. All they have to do is look up toward the sky.

TRACY: I'd feel a lot brighter if we sold our stock!

ALEX: Certainly richer! We missed our chance.

MARINA: One chance. There will be others.

HENRY: Once they clear you of their internal investigations, that stock is going to soar back up where it belongs.

TRACY: How can you be so sure? The market is so fickle.

HENRY: Yes, but...

ALEX: I know, I know! Allow me. *(Short beat:)* Talent is unstoppable.

(End of Scene 4.)

SCENE 5

(TV. Local news. Rita Storey is standing by with Duke Manning, and has late breaking news!)

RITA: We interrupt the regular scheduled program with late breaking news! The internal investigation at Advance, Incorporated is over, and Miss Tracy has been declared innocent! Clear of all allegations of fraud. How is this possible, Duke?

DUKE: Reverse age discrimination is what my grandpa would call voodoo economics. In all honesty, we really shouldn't be so surprised. In some countries and in olden days, men and women often married, had children and led tribes into battle before the age of eighteen. It's only in the so-called advanced nations that some adults feel they must get three school degrees before they are old enough to marry and move out of their parents' home. It's bull. If we're not careful, we're liable to brainwash our future away.

RITA: Don't forget, people died a lot younger then too.

DUKE: True, but there's no telling what a young man and young woman can accomplish if you don't box them in, don't lower your standards. I should know, I started working in my father's factory at fifteen. He didn't pay me too well, he was afraid of nepotism charges and it wasn't a public company then, but there wasn't a day he didn't express supreme confidence in me. He always acted like I had something to say even when I didn't. Even when I sighed and said nothing. There wasn't a day where he didn't ask me, Son, what do you think?

RITA: And look where you are today.

DUKE: Come work for me, Miss Tracy.

RITA: Did I hear correctly? You're offering Miss Tracy a job? What kind of job? Is this legal?

DUKE: Miss Tracy, I know you've had a lot of disadvantages. Me too, believe it or not. You can't get through life without some scars. But we can't change the past, we can only change the future. If you agree, have dinner with me. But this time, you have to promise to stay for the entire meal, appetizer to dessert.

RITA: What do you think, Miss Tracy? Prickly pear reporters want to know!

(End of Scene 5.)

SCENE 6

(Tracy's home. Tracy is trying to get her father to sign papers for her.)

HENRY: I'm not sure I can do this.

TRACY: It's perfectly legal. Duke says so, and he ought to know.

HENRY: Yeah, but I'm not sure it's fair. I feel that if I accept full responsibility for you and your actions, I should be entitled to know what's going on.

TRACY: Don't you trust me?

HENRY: Corporate governance, corporate fiduciary responsibility, it's all so complicated. I need more time. Guidance.

TRACY: Funny, how you didn't mind before.

(DOORBELL RINGS.)

HENRY: Oh, that must be our buyer. I invited him over for appetizers. Alex, door.

TRACY: Appetizers?

HENRY: Least I could do for someone paying thirty-five grand over asking. Alex, bring out the cheese and crackers.

TRACY: You hate cheese. Cheese is for mice.

HENRY: Behave.

(Alex escorts Christopher Brennan in.)

ALEX: I believe we've all met. Please, make yourselves comfortable.

CHRISTOPHER: Good afternoon.

TRACY: Are you the new buyer?

CHRISTOPHER: Indeed, I am.

TRACY: I can't believe you would want to live here.

CHRISTOPHER: I don't. I bought it for you and your family. To do as you wish.

HENRY: So we can still sell? That was our agreement.

CHRISTOPHER: As you wish.

ALEX: We wish. Dad and I found a bigger house with a swimming pool! Fresh start!

TRACY: I don't want your pity.

CHRISTOPHER: How dare you accuse me of doing things out of pity. I'm simply not that mature.

TRACY: No, you're not.

ALEX: Marcona almonds?

CHRISTOPHER: Please. We are both nuts. I'm sorry.

TRACY: I never lied to you.

CHRISTOPHER: I know, but I still couldn't have any contact with you until the auditors and the lawyers went over all the paperwork. Investors were threatening to sue us both for hiring you, and firing you. It was a zoo but the one thing Duke and I agreed on was that clearing your name and the firm's reputation deserved the highest priority.

TRACY: Duke offered me a job.

CHRISTOPHER: Your father told me.

HENRY: I wanted you to keep your options open.

CHRISTOPHER: Love for you to come back and work for me. You can have your old job back, or if you want a change of scenery, we'll find something new for you to do. I'll even throw in some driving lessons in your new Porsche.

TRACY: Really? A new Porsche?

CHRISTOPHER: Used. Pre-certified. Don't want to spoil you.

HENRY: Take it! And loan your father the car. After you ask, "How much?"

ALEX: And when you can get your brother a car and a job. Zoom zoom!

CHRISTOPHER: Took the liberty of ordering you some license plates.

(License plates read: TEEN MOGUL.)

TRACY: Teen Mogul. I like.

CHRISTOPHER: That's you.

TRACY: What if I want to go to college?

HENRY: Excuse me, what for? People go to college to get a plum job. He's offering you a plum job.

CHRISTOPHER: If you really want to go to college, which I'm not saying you should —

ALEX: Skip college.

CHRISTOPHER: — but speaking from personal experience, I highly recommend climbing to the top of the ivy and electing a free fall drop, it gives you a rush and elevates you to cult status figuredom. The school ends up giving you an honorary degree and it makes you the talk of cocktail parties. Forever, people will drop their jaw and say, you dropped out of where?

TRACY: Just what I need, more notoriety.

CHRISTOPHER: Some people sparkle like diamonds in the limelight. Promise me you'll give me serious consideration.

HENRY: She promises, but we haven't discussed salary. Benefits.

ALEX: More cheese? Sometimes, change is soft. Sweet. Smelly. Sometimes, change even comes with holes. Streaks of blue.

CHRISTOPHER: Sublime. I'll take another slice.

HENRY: Change tastes good. Enriching.

ALEX: Muscle-building.

CHRISTOPHER: You know what you want to do?

TRACY: Whatever I do, I promise, tomorrow, tomorrow and tomorrow, I will run faster, stretch my arms farther, and one fine morning, if I should find myself borne against the current, borne back ceaselessly into the past, drowning in despair— well, I imagine I would bounce back. I'd have to. Because I'm Teen Mogul. I'm Mostly Likely To Bounce. Because I believe in the green light.

(End of play.)

The Author Speaks

Are any characters modeled after real life or historical figures?
Yes, and no. All the characters in *Teen Mogul* are fictional, but some characters are modeled on composites of real people, and some situations are based on fact. For example, I really was a minor when I was nominated on the board of directors. I really did have to ask my father to sign papers accepting accountability even though he could not be privy to the inner sanctum, could not attend the actual board meetings. I thought it was so cool when I used to fly from Georgetown University based in Washington, D.C., to Akron, Ohio for board meetings. Christopher Brennan and Duke Manning are based on real entrepreneurs and corporate raiders that I've met, worked with, and read about. I do draw inspiration from Steve Jobs, Oprah Winfrey. The company I worked for went out of business so I named Christopher's company Advance, Incorporated as a tribute. And it is true, guilty as charged, I love "word play." I named the reporter Rita Storey for the pun, Read A Story.

What inspired you to write this play?
Teen Mogul is inspired by my real life story. When my mother abandoned us, the lights went completely out. Ashamed, embarrassed, depressed, we tried to keep it a secret, tried to "save face," but somehow everybody knew. What made it worse was our increased economic hardship. My mother took off with some savings, and two household incomes became one. We teetered on financial ruin, and plans to join the ranks of the Ivy League vanished for my brother and me. I could only wallow so long before I decided I had to do something. I hailed a cab, and invested my babysitting money in the stock market. I also called business executives I met through Junior

Achievement, and asked for work. That is how I landed at Advance, Incorporated as the Director of Market Research, and was later nominated on the board of directors. Since becoming a professional writer, I tend to forget, or discount those days, but when I teach, and share this story with my students, their jaws always drop to the floor. My students and countless others urged me to write this play, in hopes of inspiring others to empower themselves, and triumph over adversity. We all start from somewhere, but it is where we want to go, and where we end up that ultimately matters.

Have you dealt with the same theme in other works that you have written?
My parents used to tell me the whole point, the only point, of coming to America was to strike it rich. They grew up poor so that was their definition of the Great American Dream. Money. Growing up poor in Ohio just intensified the pressure for me and my brother to make their voyage worth it. After all, they sacrificed their families, their language, and ultimately their marriage so we could have a better life. They often threatened to send me back to China if I didn't follow the money: "We didn't come to America for you to be a starving artist. We could have left you in China for that!" Thus, it was very difficult for me to pursue my own dreams. In *Bullfighting*, Annie struggles with the ghost of Ernest Hemingway and the desire to quit her job. So naturally, the American Dream is one of my favorite themes. I wrestle with its definition, its power, how does one achieve it, I've even personified the Great American Dream as god spelled GAD.

I have extensive experience as the fish out of water, the outsider, the underdog so I often play with those themes, and explore the various outcomes. My play *Junk Bonds* explores how Diana copes as the first Asian American female bond trader on her trading desk, on Wall Street. My monologue *Pretty For An Asian Girl* is inspired by a true comment a high school senior made to me: "You're pretty for an Asian Girl." I remember thinking what does that mean? Is that a compliment? I was too polite and insecure back then to say anything. Many years later, when asked to write a monologue for Asian American youth, I revisited that line and let it inspire me. Another theme I play with is expectations, preconceived notions and stereotypes. I wrote about that in *My Superpower*, a monologue about an Asian American male named Stan Lee. These monologues are published in an anthology *One on One: Playing with a Purpose – Monologues for Kids 7-15*, Applause books.

What writers have had the most profound effect on your style?
Teen Mogul pays tribute to one of my favorite novels, F. Scott Fitzgerald's *The Great Gatsby*. When I worked at New York City's City Hall, I was nicknamed the Hemingway of Memos so Ernest Hemingway must have seeped into my subconscious. I also love more writers than I can possibly name: Barbara Kingsolver, Louise Erdrich, Sherman Alexie, Don Lee. I read as much as I can, and across most genres. I read cookbooks, biographies, plays, novels, whatever catches and holds my interest. My English teacher from high school often sends me books, so I still buy hard copy once in a while so I can trade.

What do you hope to achieve with this work?
I hope *Teen Mogul* inspires everyone to dream big, and reach for the sky. To believe in him, or herself, to not be afraid to leap for the brass ring. I purposely didn't give Alex and Tracy last names, because I wanted Alex and Tracy to be anybody, portrayed by anybody. Throughout our lives, there are times

we all feel insecure, discouraged, beaten down, and we all face obstacles but it is my hope that *Teen Mogul* reminds us to always believe in ourselves, and keep moving forward. Writing this play has certainly helped me many years later, as I remember a time when I didn't take no for a final answer. *Teen Mogul* is a friendly reminder that it doesn't matter who you are, where you are in life, you can never give up.

What were the biggest challenges involved in the writing of this play?

My biggest challenge on *Teen Mogul* was probably taking a very sad event — my mother's abandonment — and writing it as a dramedy/comedy. True comedy, however, is said to come from tragedy. Tragedy + time = comedy. Looking back, I think humor was how I survived. It was my armor, my coping mechanism.

I also wanted to create roles that were open to any and all ethnicities. That's why the main characters do not have last names. I wanted to drive home the point that this family could be Chinese American, Armenian American, Irish American, anyone.

The world is constantly changing so it was difficult to decide what product Tracy makes as new products and trends are constantly coming to market, rendering many products and services obsolete. The fast pace of technology also means we have more *Teen Moguls* today than we had when I was growing up.

What inspired you to become a playwright?

When I was a little girl, I was smitten by stage and screen. I wanted so badly to be an actress. Against my parents' wishes, I signed up for Drama Club, and classes at the local community theatre. My parents were thrilled when I found so few roles for Asian American girls. I was offered all the stereotypes—Dragon Lady, Masseuse, Laundromat Owner, Lotus Blossom, Math Nerd. Every year I was cast as the Chinese Dancer in Tchaikovsky's *Nutcracker* ballet and had to bow in a circle, coolie hat and all, for the entire length of "Tea." I was constantly told some version of "Dance Ten, Looks Too Chinese." My budding career hit rock bottom when I was offered the chance to just stand there, and look pretty exotic as a "flowerpot."

I completely abandoned the idea of a career in the arts when my mother left because the pressure to make money intensified a million-fold. Growing up without, I knew I had to find a way to support myself. It wasn't until much later, when I lost my job working for NYC Mayor Dinkins because Mayor Dinkins lost his job to Mayor Giuliani, that I started to write in my downtime. Mostly to keep the blues away, as being unemployed during the holidays can be very depressing. I started writing short stories, and everyone in my writing workshop said, "This is a play! Turn this story into a play." I did, and that's when it all clicked. I realized when I wasn't working, I spent much of my free time and savings catching shows on and off-Broadway.

How did you research the subject?
This will sound terribly geeky, but I have always loved business and writing. Think Alex P. Keaton in that TV show, *Family Ties*. I used to be a bond trader on Wall Street, I worked for NYC Mayor David Dinkins, and I have an MBA from the University of Chicago Booth School of Business, so I keep pretty current with business news, the world economy and the market. I often read bios and letters of great people to help inspire me to be a better person, to stay positive. I also had to revisit my mother-less past, painful, and decide what

was most important for this story. Flipped through old photo albums, and gasped at my younger self sporting a suit and a big hair-do, giving speeches on the miracles of free enterprise.

Are any characters modeled after real life or historical figures?
All the characters are fictional. Duke Manning and Christopher Brennan are modeled after real life business entrepreneurs and corporate raiders. Miss Sarah Nutter is a composite of all the great teachers I've had throughout my life.

Shakespeare gave advice to the players in *Hamlet*; if you could give advice to your cast what would it be?
My advice is have fun. Be bold. Laugh. Don't forget to "play." Often in our pursuit to make our plays mean something, to resonate, we forget to put the "play" back into play. We all want to strut and fret upon a stage and signify *some*thing that sometimes we take our plays too seriously. We forget that laughter is revolutionary. You cannot force someone to think something is funny, or fun. Laughter, having fun, playing opens our eyes, our hearts, and new worlds. The "play" is the thing. If you "play," they will come.

About the Author

Lucy Wang writes, teaches, and occasionally performs. Her plays have been performed all over the world. Wang has also written two short films (one of which she directed), and sold a pilot to Disney. Her awards include the Kennedy Center Fund for New American Plays, Best New Political Social Play from the Katherine and Lee Chilcote Foundation, Berrilla Kerr Foundation, James Thurber Fellowship, CAPE's New Writers TV Award, NATPE Diversity Fellow, William and Flora Hewlett Foundation Honorary Fellow, Annenberg

Community Beach House Writer in Residence. Wang has taught at many fine institutions including Firestone High, Marshall High, University of Southern California, Ohio State University, American Conservatory Theater. Her manuscripts are archived at the Huntington Library in San Marino. She is a member of The Alliance of Los Angeles Playwrights, the Los Angeles Female Playwrights Initiative, and on the faculty of E-script.

About YouthPLAYS

YouthPLAYS (www.youthplays.com) is a publisher of award-winning professional dramatists and talented new discoveries, each with an original theatrical voice, and all dedicated to expanding the vocabulary of theatre for young actors and audiences. On our website you'll find one-act and full-length plays and musicals for teen and pre-teen (and even college) actors, as well as duets and monologues for competition. Many of our authors' works have been widely produced at high schools and middle schools, youth theatres and other TYA companies, both amateur and professional, as well as at elementary schools, camps, churches and other institutions serving young audiences and/or actors worldwide. Most are intended for performance by young people, while some are intended for adult actors performing for young audiences.

YouthPLAYS was co-founded by professional playwrights Jonathan Dorf and Ed Shockley. It began merely as an additional outlet to market their own works, which included a substantial body of award-winning published and unpublished plays and musicals. Those interested in their published plays were directed to the respective publishers' websites, and unpublished plays were made available in electronic form. But when they saw the desperate need for material for young actors and audiences—coupled with their experience that numerous quality plays for young people weren't finding a home—they made the decision to represent the work of other playwrights as well. Dozens and dozens of authors are now members of the YouthPLAYS family, with scripts available both electronically and in traditional acting editions. We continue to grow as we look for exciting and challenging plays and musicals for young actors and audiences.

About ProduceaPlay.com

Let's put up a play! Great idea! But producing a play takes time, energy and knowledge. While finding the necessary time and energy is up to you, ProduceaPlay.com is a website designed to assist you with that third element: knowledge.

Created by YouthPLAYS' co-founders, Jonathan Dorf and Ed Shockley, ProduceaPlay.com serves as a resource for producers at all levels as it addresses the many facets of production. As Dorf and Shockley speak from their years of experience (as playwrights, producers, directors and more), they are joined by a group of award-winning theatre professionals and experienced teachers from the world of academic theatre, all making their expertise available for free in the hope of helping this and future generations of producers, whether it's at the school or university level, or in community or professional theatres.

The site is organized into a series of major topics, each of which has its own page that delves into the subject in detail, offering suggestions and links for further information. For example, Publicity covers everything from Publicizing Auditions to How to Use Social Media to Posters to whether it's worth hiring a publicist. Casting details Where to Find the Actors, How to Evaluate a Resume, Callbacks and even Dealing with Problem Actors. You'll find guidance on your Production Timeline, The Theater Space, Picking a Play, Budget, Contracts, Rehearsing the Play, The Program, House Management, Backstage, and many other important subjects.

The site is constantly under construction, so visit often for the latest insights on play producing, and let it help make your play production dreams a reality.

More from YouthPLAYS

Long Joan Silver by Arthur M. Jolly

Comedy. 90-100 minutes. 6-15 males, 8-20 females (14-30 performers possible, plus extras).

The classic tale of buried treasure—and the original one-legged pirate with a parrot—gets a comic makeover even while it explores discrimination, privilege and greed. Unlike in Robert Louis Stevenson's book, women are front and center as *Long Joan Silver*'s young Jim Hawkins comes of age during the fateful voyage of the Hispaniola and the clash between an all-female pirate crew and Squire Trelawney, Doctor Livesey and the domineering Captain Smollett.

The Old New Kid by Adam J. Goldberg

Comedy. 30-40 minutes. 2-9+ males, 3-10+ females (8-30+ performers possible).

It's the half-day of school before Thanksgiving break, and current "new kid" Alan Socrates Bama just wants to get through the day. But when a new-new kid arrives, things change. Alan has three hours to find the meaning of Thanksgiving, survive elementary school politics, battle for his identity, and spell the word "cornucopia" in this *Peanuts*-flavored comedy for kids of all ages.

Kitty Steals a Dog by Keegon Schuett

Comedy. 22-30 minutes. 2 males, 2 females. Suitable for middle school and older.

Meet Kitty, a reluctant ballerina. Enter Liam, uptight teenage lemonade salesman. Kitty has lost her dog. Liam has a crush on the girl next door. They don't have much in common. Maybe nothing at all. But when this unlikely dynamic duo joins forces to steal the girl next door's dog and win her heart for Liam, will it be mission accomplished, or will this risky thing called friendship crash and burn and unleash complete canine chaos on their unsuspecting suburban neighborhood?

Clay by Carol S. Lashof
Dramedy. 30-40 minutes. 2 males, 2 females.

Aaron, Zeta and Will are as different as three students could be. One works tirelessly yet struggles to pass. One excels by cutting every corner, and one attends school intermittently despite exceptional intelligence and creativity. Forced to interact by a group assignment, they confront themselves, each other and the magic of molding clay.

Dear Chuck by Jonathan Dorf
Dramedy. 30-40 minutes. 8-30+ performers (gender flexible).

Teenagers are typically caught in the middle—they're not quite adults, but they're definitely no longer children. Through a series of scenes and monologues, we meet an eclectic group of teen characters who are trying to communicate with that wannabe special someone, coping with a classmate's suicide, battling controlling parents, swimming for that island of calm in the stormy sea of technology—and many others. What they all have in common is the search for their "Chuck," that elusive moment of knowing who you are. Also available in a 60-70 minute version.

Lockdown by Julia Edwards
Dramedy. 75-90 minutes. 4-6 males, 9-11 females (15 performers total).

It's just another day in the CliffsNotes Library until a siren sounds, the doors lock, and the not-so-studious students discover they are trapped. Did the high-tech security system malfunction again? Is this a sinister state-sanctioned experiment? Then someone hears a gunshot (he thinks), a freaked out substitute teacher is found barricaded in the bathroom, and Crazy Lily has a diabetic seizure. In a claustrophobic pressure-cooker of fear, paranoia, and social strife, this motley crew of hackers, delinquents, surfer dudes, and prom queens must rise above the chaos to save a life and discover the meaning of tolerance along the way.

Made in the USA
Monee, IL
09 January 2021